For all of the professionals out there –
who want to be a role model for their
children; who see their professional
skills as tools for business and social
change; and who need a better answer
when asked: "What are you doing to
make the world a better place?"

*The design of this book was underwritten by
Ashoka (www.ashoka.org), innovators for the public.*

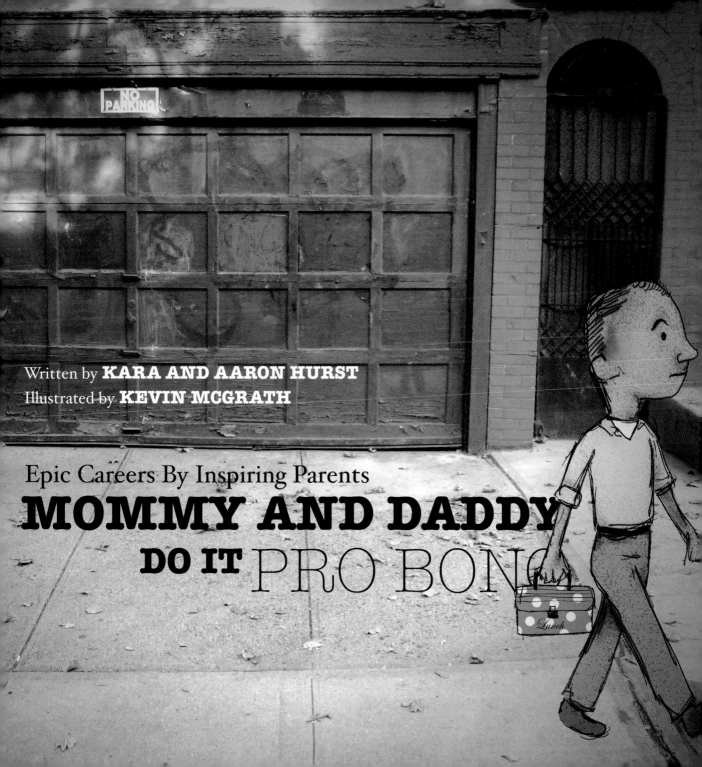

Written by **KARA AND AARON HURST**

Illustrated by **KEVIN MCGRATH**

Epic Careers By Inspiring Parents

MOMMY AND DADDY
DO IT PRO BONO

Mommy and Daddy Do It Pro Bono

Written by Kara Hartnett Hurst & Aaron Hurst

Illustrated by Kevin McGrath

Photos donated by Kevin McGrath, Allison Lynch & Mick Minard.

Copyright © 2009 by the Taproot Foundation (tapfound, Inc.)

First Edition.

Printed in Canada on recycled paper. All rights reserved.

ISBN: 978-0-615-26839-2

Library of Congress Control Number: 2009900827

10 9 8 7 6 5 4 3 2 1

Taproot Foundation Press

466 Geary Street, Suite 200

San Francisco, California 94102

www.taprootfoundation.org

www.doitprobono.org

I also do pro bono work by traveling around the world to help kids who can't pay for their own doctor.

My mommy is an accountant for a great big toy store.
She counts ALL their money.

My daddy makes ads for companies to help them sell things. He says it is marketing. I saw his ad on TV for a new car.

My daddy is a graphic designer. When people write books, he makes the pictures. The pictures make the book exciting, so more people want to buy it.

My mommy is a lawyer. She helps people fight using words so they don't hit each other.

My mommy is a consultant. She flies around the world to help companies solve difficult problems.

Sometimes she writes pro bono for the place where the grandmas and grandpas live. She makes the letters really big LIKE THIS, so everyone can read it.

He also flew to Africa to help villages get clean drinking water, so nobody gets sick anymore.

He uses his skills pro bono to help injured soldiers get new jobs when they come back from war.

He also built a website for a group that helps to save elephants and other animals.

My mommy is an architect. She designed this cool hotel near her office.

About the Writers and Illustrator

Kara and Aaron live in Brooklyn with their kids, Lola B and Max. Kara is a global leader in corporate social reponsibility. Aaron is the founder of the Taproot Foundation, a nonprofit leading the pro bono service movement.

Kevin also resides in Brooklyn, where he works part-time as an artist and full-time as an advocate for children with special needs.